The FAMILY CIRCUS PARADE

By

Bil Keane

Andrews, McMeel & Parker Inc.
A Universal Press Syndicate Company

Kansas City ● New York

ISBN: 0-8362-1221-5

Library of Congress Catalog Card Number: 83-73611

ATTENTION: SCHOOLS AND BUSINESSES

Andrews, McMeel & Parker books are available at quantity discounts with bulk purchase for educational, business, or sales promotional use. For information, please write to: Special Sales Department, Andrews, McMeel & Parker, 4400 Johnson Drive, Fairway, Kansas 66205.

FEATURING OUR BIG TOP PERFORMERS

CLOWNS

TRAPEZE ARTIST

BAREBACK RIDERS

TATOOED LADY

WILD ANIMALS

PERFORMING BARE

IT'S OSCAR TIME

BEST SONG

COSTUME DESIGN

BEST PICTURE

SPECIAL EFFECTS

ANIMATED SHORT SUBJECT

BEST ACTOR

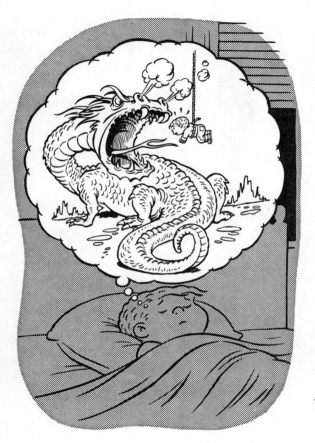

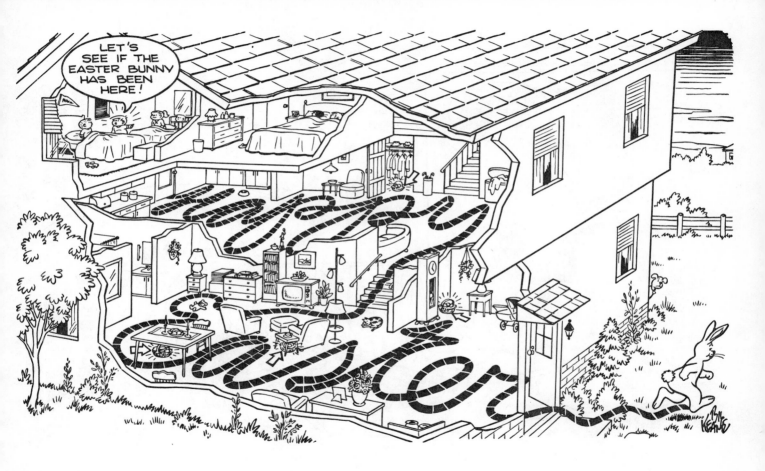

Occasionally seven-year-old Billy fills in for Daddy. Here are some of his pages.

Mommy Watching Her Figure

Jeffy Lying in a Bed

Dolly is Ruthless

Buoys and Gulls Together

Daddy Meating a Dead Lion

PJ Kicking the Habit

Good Knight!

My Daddy the Runner
By Billy

I think the hardest part of running is the faces you have to make when you're done.

Once in a while the weather ruins everything

Poor Daddy -- He says jogging is a very lonely sport.

Sometimes he sprints really FAST!

He doesn't run every day because there's a lot of studying to be done

He claims running is good for taking off weight.

GROWN-UPS PARTY

SPIED ON AND DRAWN BY Billy

Daddy mixed up a magic potion in the punch bowl.

Jeffy was the food taster when nobody was looking.

You picked a fine time to leave me, Lucille...

The daddies had some kind of a contest to see who could yell the loudest

Mr. Spero took a nice nap in PJ's room.

Did you hear the one about...

The daddies held a lot of long meetings in the kitchen

Then my little Lisa said...

Yesterday Jeffy and PJ were..

What are those guys doing in the kitchen?

The mommies talked and talked and talked...

Uncle Bob slipped a disc trying to disco

Dolly tried out all the coats and handbags that were on the bed

G'nite!

Daddy had to say goodbye to all the guests before they left.

OUR SITTER as seen by me. (Billy)

Testing out Mommy's Clothes (they don't fit)

Putting PJ in for a nap

Bringing in the mail

Hows everything there in Wyoming?

Talking on The phone with her sister

Drinking out of Daddy's little measuring glass

Visiting with her usual gang: Mike, Phil, Dinah, Merv, etc.

Putting away my drawings of her where they'll be safe. (But I'll do them over)

Here is one more page where little Billy borrows the dotted line format to depict his version of Daddy's early morning routine.

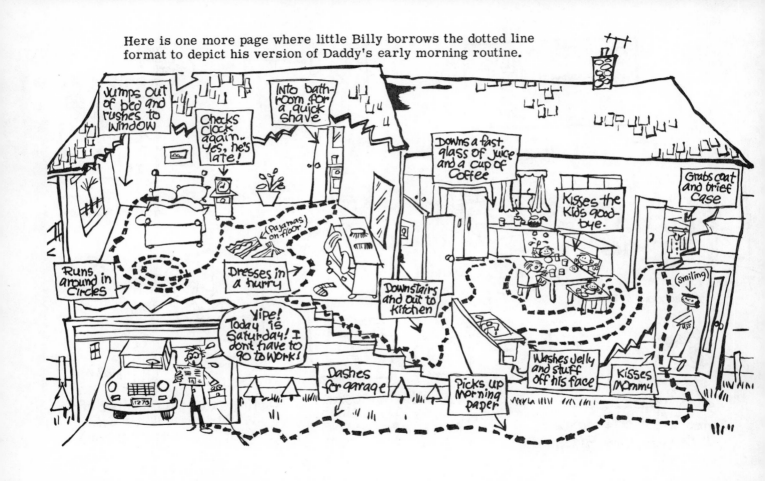

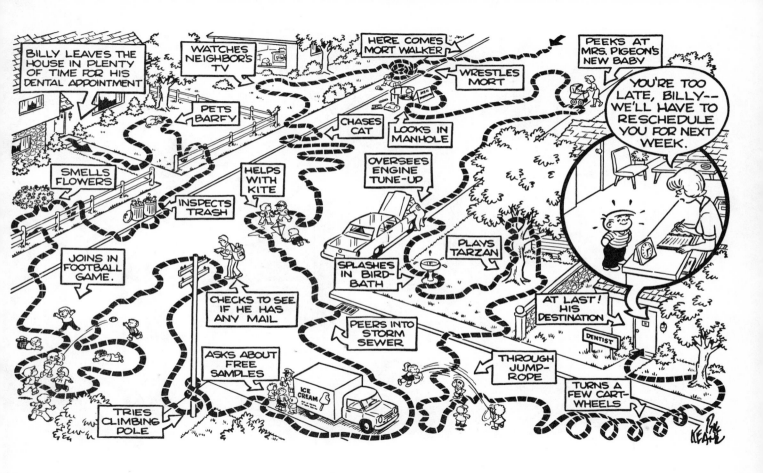

...AND NOW THE WEATHER

TEMPERATURE ABOVE NORMAL

SON RISES AT 5:46 A.M.

WARMING TREND

INTERMITTENT SHOWERS

CLOUDBURST

FOGGY

FLOODS

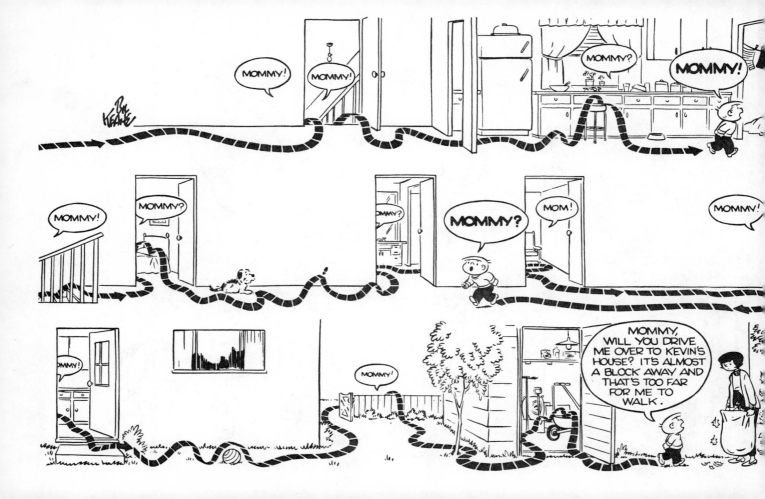

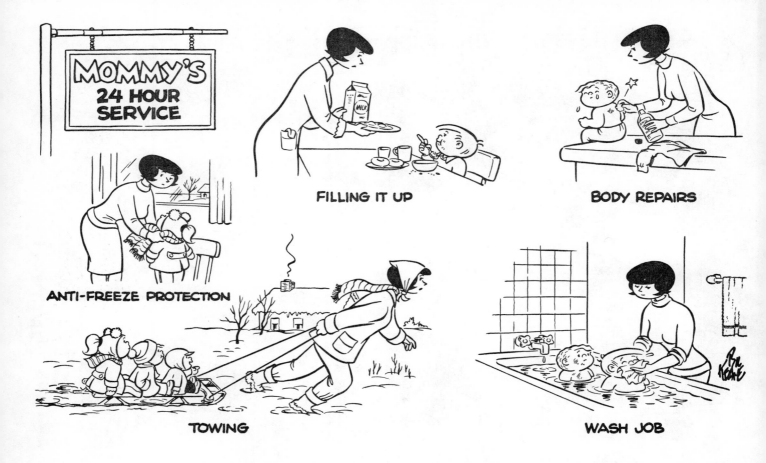

MOMMY'S 24 HOUR SERVICE

FILLING IT UP

BODY REPAIRS

ANTI-FREEZE PROTECTION

TOWING

WASH JOB

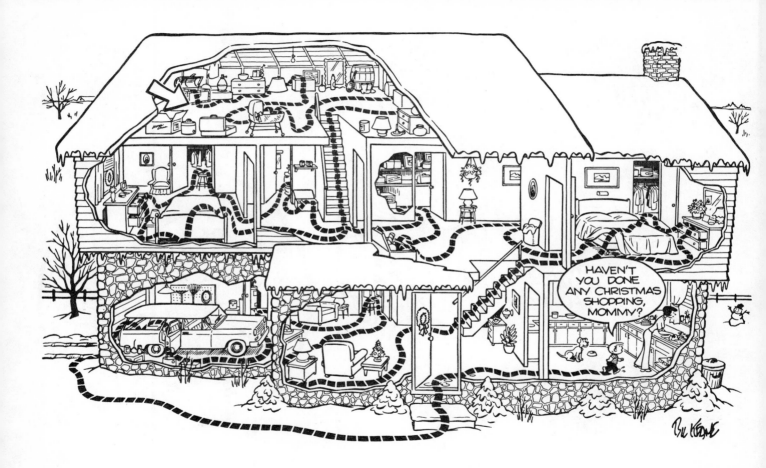

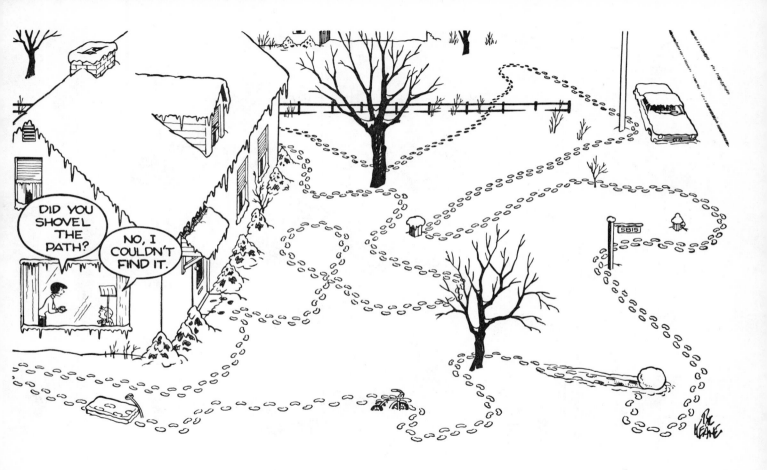

SLIPPERY WHEN WET

WATCH FOR BUMP

YIELD

DOWN GRADE AHEAD

PEDESTRIAN CROSSING

DO NOT ENTER

SOFT SHOULDER